An Otley Run

A verse novella

Joe Williams

This is not an
instruction manual

Published by Half Moon Books 2018,
OWF Press Community Interest Company
Otley Courthouse, Courthouse Street, Otley, West Yorkshire
LS21 3AN

www.halfmoonbooks.co.uk

Cover illustration and map: Neil Morrison

ISBN 978-0-9957642-9-3

Printed and bound by
ImprintDigital.com, Seychelles Farm, Upton Pyne, Exeter, Devon EX5 5HY
info@imprintdigital.com

Acknowledgements

'Overture' was adapted from the poem 'An Otley Run', which first appeared in the pamphlet 'Killing the Piano' published by Half Moon Books in 2017.

'Epilogue' was first published as 'Epilogue to an Otley Run' by Eunoia Review.

Thanks to Anzir Boodoo, Lindsay Brown, Mark Connors, Alicia Fernández, Maria Ferguson, Neil Fulwood, Gaia Holmes, Gill Lambert, Rob Langley, Neil Morrison, James Nash, Marina Poppa, Henry Raby, Chris Thorpe, David Williams, Paula Williams and Michael Yates for their support and suggestions that helped in the creation of this book, to Roz Fairclough, Jane Kite and Peter White at Half Moon Books for providing the opportunity to inflict it on the public, and to the pubs and the thousands of anonymous Otley Runners who inspired it.

For more information about Joe Williams and the Otley Run, see www.anotleyrun.com and www.joewilliams.co.uk

An Otley Run

Contents

Foreword

The first time I ever heard of the Otley Run pub crawl was shortly after moving to Leeds as a student in the nineties. It was, I was told, a classic way for the city's students to celebrate a birthday, the end of exams, or simply the freedom of youth.

It's all very different now. It's much longer, for one thing. Several of the pubs usually included in today's Otley Run, and in this book, didn't exist in 1992. The Dry Dock and Headingley Taps both opened during my time at university, and shortly afterwards the Feast & Firkin appeared, in the building which now houses The Library. Arc and The Box came later, while Strawbs has transformed over the years from a café to a bar.

As students, we'd never have got that far anyway. More likely we'd make it to The Eldon before retiring to the safety of the Old Bar in Leeds University Union, perhaps followed by the notorious student disco known as the Poly Bop, if we were up for a late night Saturday.

You wouldn't have caught us wearing fancy dress either. The costumes didn't appear, for the most part, until the late nineties and early noughties, along with the expansion of the route and the accompanying marketing efforts that have helped to transform the Otley Run from a local students' rite of passage into a nationally known pub crawl. Nowadays dozens of stag dos, hen parties, birthday gatherings, hundreds of visitors from all over the UK, can be seen doing the Run every weekend, especially during the summer, alongside the students, with whom it is still popular.

We nineties kids can't claim to have invented it. The Otley Run grew out of an older pub crawl, the Headingley Mile, and while the route has remained fairly consistent since its explosion in popularity, it continues to evolve. I am writing this in September 2018, two weeks after Arc's rebranding and rebirth as Manahatta. Trio – a venue which wasn't always considered part of the Otley Run, but which was certainly included by some parties, and which is mentioned in the book – closed suddenly last year, and remains vacant. Four of the other pubs have been substantially refurbished within the last eighteen months, while JD Wetherspoon appear to have failed in their attempt to open a new pub on Otley Road, having had a licensing appeal rejected.

Despite the variations, the principle remains the same. Revellers should have a drink in every pub on, or very close to, the Otley Road, from Woodies in Far Headingley to The Dry Dock on the edge of the city centre, next to Leeds Beckett University's City Campus – minus, that is, a few establishments which prefer to exclude Otley Runners.

It has been many years since I've attempted a full Otley Run, but I do pay an occasional visit, at least, to many of its pubs, and having lived in and near Headingley for most of the last 25 years, I see a lot of these people. They might be entertaining, astonishing, amusing, infuriating or concerning, but they are rarely uninteresting to someone who enjoys the great pastime of people-watching. You may have seen them too, and perhaps have been one of them yourself. If not, then reading this book might make you want to join in the fun someday. It might, on the other hand, make you want to stay away forever.

Whichever it is, I hope that as you read you will be able to recall, or imagine, the magic and the madness of the legendary Otley Run.

—Joe Williams

The Otley Run

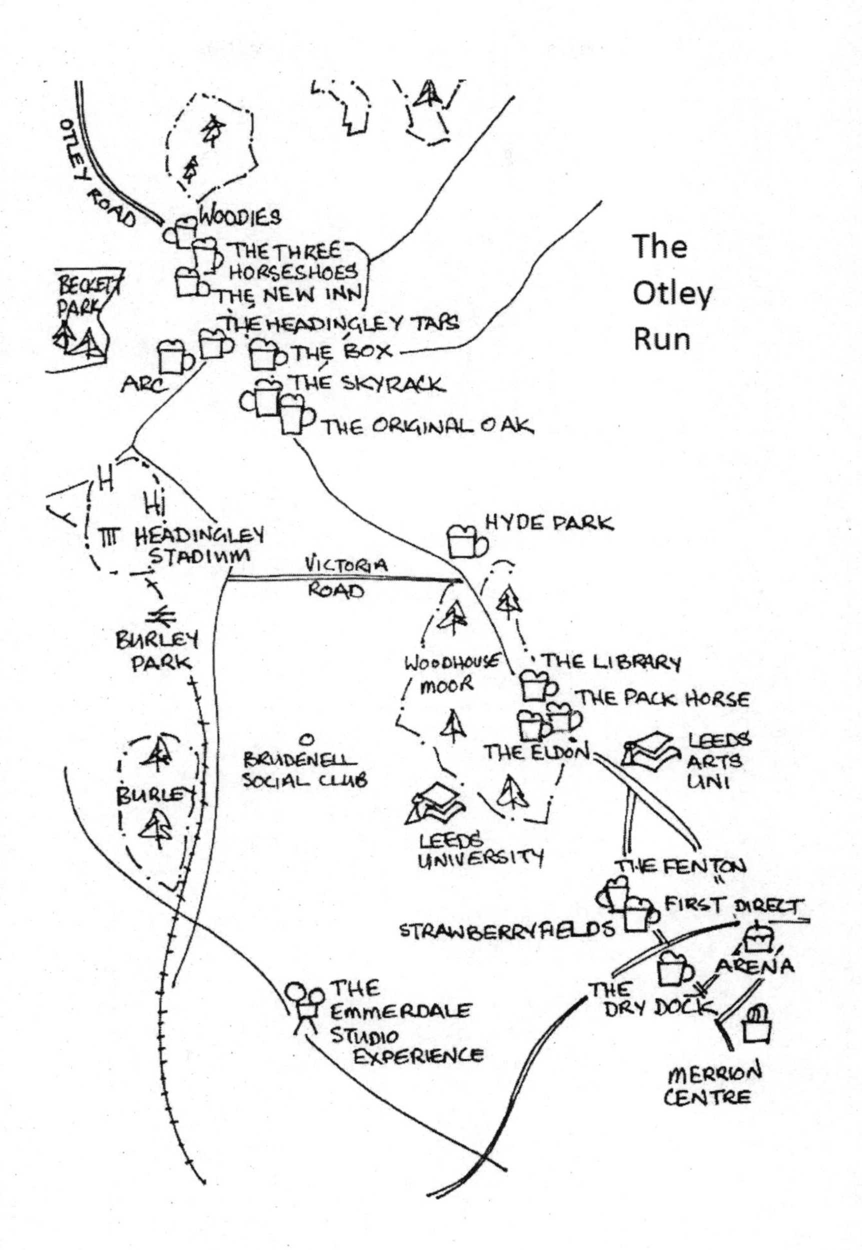

Overture

Woodies.
That's where you start, and we'll have no arguing
about the Stables or the Village.
Those aren't pubs, they're hotels.
And be there by two o'clock, latest,
if you want to make it through alive.

The Three Horseshoes.
You might hear the mumbling,
the locals grumbling under their breath,
as if they weren't used to this by now.
As if *their* pub didn't depend on you.

The New Inn.
Here we must mention the costumes,
as you drink by the roadside
as Snow White or Julius Caesar.
In my day it wouldn't have crossed our minds.
It's all but mandatory now.

Arcadia?
Forget it.
No large groups, no fancy dress.
You are not welcome here.
The regulars chuckle as eight James Bonds
are ejected for dressing too smart.

At this point Darth Vader will suggest
the Arc, the Taps or Trio.
Some will shun the Dark Side.
Not on the Otley Road, not on the Otley Run.
Stay as you are, and head for The Box
for the next one.

The Skyrack and The Oak.
The beating hearts of Headingley.
Take them in the order you choose,
with a hop across the road,
a cheer for Fred Flintstone,
who won't wait for the lights to change.

The Hyde Park.
It's a fair walk for ten Where's Wallys,
cloned in single file.
There's only supposed to be one of him, idiots.
That's the whole fucking point.

The Library.
Are you sick by now? Are you tired?
Are you wishing you hadn't agreed to this?
Elvis is face down on the table,
and if he doesn't die in the toilet
you'll have to prop him up when he leaves the building.

The Pack Horse.
The group has thinned out,
thanks to dropouts and dawdlers.
You still barely fit into this place.
Cleopatra vomits into her handbag

The Eldon.
Finally someone asks:
Is coming, blacked up,
as the Jamaican bobsleigh team
just a little bit racist?

The Fenton and Strawbs.
Neighbours on the home straight.
Just to get this far
makes you some kind of winner,
like the guy copping off with Catwoman,
despite being dressed as a Teletubby.

The Dry Dock.
This, I suggest, should be your final port.
And even if Superman still has his strength
and Tinkerbell's wings aren't broken,
please ignore Lord Vader and his latest bright idea:
'Let's go to Pryzm!'

The Spice Girls ride
the 97 bus.
Emma hits the button: STOP

Act I

Woodies

I'm the first one here.
I knew I would be.
Not even early, just on time,
but the lads are always late.
They'll be watching the match,
waiting for the whistle
that says they can leave the sofa.

I buy a pint and sit on my own
at the biggest table in the pub.
I sip and wait, wait and sip,
feeling a clown in my home-made toga.
Eventually the lads show up
in twos and threes and fours,
and I relax a little, now I'm not
the only Roman in the room.
Or are we supposed to be Greeks?
I don't think we ever specified,
and I don't think this lot care.

Ash is last, as usual.
The first thing he says
is, 'Nice tits!' to the girl on the bar,
who doesn't react except to make sure
he's the last one to be served.

I’m already thinking
I should have come up
with some sort of excuse.

The Three Horseshoes

I'm already thinking
I should have come up
with some sort of excuse.

We're only on our second drink
and my cowgirl chaps are pissing me off.
I thought I'd be comfortable wearing this.
I was wrong.
At least I'm not showing off half my arse
like Sarah the fairy fucking queen,
or her, there, Maria Sharapova,
whatever her real name is.

I'd hoped there'd be more folk I know,
but there's only Sarah and Rachael,
nobody else from the office.
Mostly Sarah's friends from school or uni,
a couple of cousins, her mum.
It's Sam, her mum. Or is it Pam?
Whatever it is, I'm glad she's here.
Saves me from being the only one over thirty
and not dressed like a prostitute.
Even Rachael's surprised me with that dress,
those black cat ears.

The naughty nurse is Charlie –
Charlotte to mummy and daddy, I'd bet –
maid of honour, as she's told us fifty times.
I don't think we're going to get on, but
she's got the rest of the day to prove me wrong.

I thought it'd all be pissheads and twats,
but there's normal people in here.
A big group there, students I guess,
led by the pink bloody panther.
But normal people as well.

It's alright, this place.
That first one wasn't bad either.
Just as I think it, in comes a group,
lads all dressed in home-made togas,
supposed to be Greeks or Romans,
I don't know.

By the time they sit down I know – wankers.
The biggest and loudest one's shouting a song
from the football or something,
his mates all laughing.

I'm glad when it's time to move on.
I hope to hell we're not going to
see much more of them.

The New Inn

It's my round, I'm told.
There's no point in arguing.
Ash has it all worked out.
He explained in the Horseshoes.
Woodies doesn't count
because we didn't get a round,
so that leaves fourteen pubs
and there's fourteen of us,
one round each.

He got the first himself –
'Captain's privilege,' he called it –
then we go through the team,
starting from the back,
so now it's my turn.

I don't think I've ever bought
fourteen drinks at once.
At least this place is cheap
and I've got it over early.
Someone could help to carry them, though.
'Safe pair of hands,' cracks Jonny,
as I spill some,
a bit too close
to a woman in a Stetson.

Danny's trying to count out the pubs.
It's a subject of debate,
but Ash has it all worked out.
'It's Arc next, then the Taps,' he says.
'Not Trio. That's a restaurant.'
'It's a bar downstairs,' says Chris,
and gets told where to go.

Danny studies the menu
and Jonny studies the girls.
'She's fit,' he says.
'She's got fit hair.'
'Who?' I ask, follow his gaze.
'Blonde, white dress, wand.'
'Not my type,' I tell him,
and look elsewhere.

Arc

Sam – it is Sam – seems nice.
Doesn't say much though.
Can't get a word in edgeways mostly.
We had a bit of a chat on the walk down here.
Work, weather, the usual
getting-to-know-you stuff.
I get the idea she's not too hot
on Dean, Sarah's groom-to-be,
but doesn't seem the type to share her thoughts.
I might share mine later on,
if the booze loosens my tongue.

God, does Charlie ever shut up?
It's non-bloody-stop.
Wittering on about herself
and other trivialities.
It's not my kind of place in here,
but at least the music
muffles her a bit.

The daft thing is, Sarah could have
whoever she wanted, more or less.
She's always got guys hovering round.
One of them toga boys already tried
chatting her up at the bar.
You'd think the tiara would give him a clue
he's on a hiding to nothing.

That other lad keeps looking as well.
The one who nearly soaked us in beer.
He looked mortified.
I don't know why.
He only got a little bit on my boot.
Polite, and a lovely smile
when he saw I wasn't bothered.

See, Sarah, you could have picked
a guy like that. Someone nice.
I would have, when I wasn't twice his age.
Or I'd have tried.
I bet you'd be more into his mate,
the loud one,
the bellend.

I notice Rachael's
looking at her watch.

The Headingley Taps

Another fourteen boys,
another fourteen pints
set down on another wooden table
on another busy day.

Another brood of hens,
another fairy bride,
drinking halfs and bottles
of I can't decide,
and I'd better take it easy,
we'll have cocktails later,
and no, I'll get these.

There'll be hundreds today
just like them.
Hop-licked strollers
on a big day out
that might be once in a lifetime,
but here
this is normal.

And they're doing alright
for this time of day.
Some of them might make it all the way,
but not him,
or her,
or him.

We can always tell
who's bored or slumping,
waiting for the wind to change,
a bite to eat to pick them up,
to skip a drink next time.
We can always tell
who never really wanted to be here.

Like Caligula
and Annie Oakley,
nursing their drinks,
looking around,
anywhere, at anything
except their friends.

Then she turns
to catch his eye and says,
'You look like you're having a right laugh.'
And he laughs.
Just a little.
Just for her.

Luigi says to Mario,
'How high can you go?'
Mario leaps.

Act II

The Box

It's Jonny's turn to get the beers.
I give him a hand with carrying,
resisting the urge to take the piss
when he spills some.

'Those girls are outside,' he says,
'we should go out there,'
but Ash says no.
I check the window and agree,
'It is quite hot in here,'
but I'm overruled.
'Some of them are fit though,'
Ash decides, and gives us a rundown
of his personal top five
and the order in which
he'd let them have sex with him.
I've stopped listening.

Five minutes later, he's forced me
into being his partner for table football.
'I need a keeper,' he says. 'Come on.'
I try to explain that the skills required
aren't exactly the same,
but I'm wasting my time.
'Shut it,' he says. 'We're white,
you cunts are stripes.
Who's got a quid?'
We win 10–5, a few of their goals
disallowed by the self-appointed ref,
who says they were spinning.

I go upstairs to the toilet,
meet the cowgirl, coming down.
'Did you win?' she asks.
I don't know what to tell her.

The Original Oak

The early evening sun's still warm.
It's nice to be outside.
Some of these pubs are too bloody busy.
The only thing is, I'm stuck on the end
of this wobbly wooden table,
Charlie beside me,
Maria Sharapova across.
Her real name's Claire, I've been reminded,
bezzie mates with Charlie.

The smoke from their fags goes up my nose,
in my eyes, as I have to listen
to them slagging off strangers.
'I wouldn't wear that with an arse that big,'
and, 'What the fuck has she done to her eyebrows?'

The boys get all their compliments,
eyed up without shame or subtlety.
Charlie declares she's two drinks from horny,
sights set on either Batman or Indiana Jones.
I'm not convinced by Batman with a beard,
but I keep it to myself.

Claire looks around the garden and asks,
'Where's them lads in the bed sheets?
A couple of them were really, really hot.'
I wonder which she means.
'Don't tell Martin,' Charlie says,
and Claire replies, 'What happens in Vegas...'
Their laughter shakes the table.

Charlie turns to me and says,
'One of them's getting friendly with you.
The cowgirl's gonna ride
some toyboy cock tonight!'
I try to hide behind my drink.
They shriek again,
louder.

I try to change the subject, ask them
questions about their lives, but
they don't seem very interested,
and honestly, neither am I.

When we leave we see the toga boys
on the other side of the crossing.
'There they are!' Charlie shouts.
'There's your boys, Claire!'
Sarah mashes the button,
though the light's already lit.
We wait, facing over the road
till the green man lets us go.

As we cross I can't help but smile,
mouth a secret hello.

The Skyrack

—I'm getting a tattoo on Monday.
—What are you gonna get?
—I'm getting Muslim writing, on my arm, here, that says 'Fuck off terrorist'.

Ash pulls his fingers down his forearm,
laughs at his own genius,
some of the lads a sycophantic echo.
I'm not sure if they all understand
why he thinks it's funny.

Jonny gives me the slightest sign,
a twitch of the head towards the door.
One at a time, him then me,
trying not to be noticed, we slip outside.
I'm hoping Ash has drunk enough
that we might get away with
a minute or two of peace.

—Jesus Christ, he's properly switched to maximum prick mode today.

Jonny's leaning against the wall.
I smile and we sit in silence a while,
watching the passers-by,
the other customers.

—How are you holding up?
—I'm OK. Could do with a break and some food.
—Yeah, same.

We settle back to silence.
It's him that breaks it again.

—What's with you and that cowboy girl?
—Cowboy girl? What do you mean? Do you think she's had gender reassignment?

Jonny looks confused.
I try to keep up my poker face,
but I don't last long.

—Shut up, you tit. You know what I mean.
—We were just chatting. She's funny. Nice. I don't think you've got much chance with her friend, though.
—Why not? Do you think she's out of my league?
—Well, for one thing, I think she's getting married, mate.
—What? Today? She's gonna be a bit fucking pissed.

He tries to look blank, but now
it's his turn failing to keep a straight face.
The laughter spreads between us.

—You knob.
—Ah well, can't win 'em all.

We don't get much more private time
before Ash comes out to find us.

—What are you cunts doing out here? Fucking bumming?

—Yes, Ash, we've been bumming, in front of all these people.
—Fuck off, sarky cunt. And get your fucking drinks down. We're off.

While we're waiting to cross the road,
we see the hens again, coming down
from the garden at The Oak.
I was wondering where they'd gone.
They must be doing these two pubs
the other way round.
The one that was top of Ash's list
shouts something. I can't hear for the traffic.

I glance along the line of their group,
take a step to the left,
making sure I cross
in the best possible place.

Hyde Park

I buy Rachael a drink.
I thought she might have left by now,
but the pizza we shared, foul as it was,
and the time it took to order, cook and eat it
have done us good.
She's turning it up a notch, in fact.
This time the wine's a large one,
and she's smiling more than I've seen her smile all day.

Charlie's two-drink prediction was right,
by the looks of the way that her and Claire
are talking to boys that they don't know.
Their confidence pulls in other girls.
I move away and sit on my own
in a corner, just a spectator,
wondering why, at the back of the pub
there's a bloke in a pink nun's habit
showing off with half-arsed press-ups
on the pool table.

Rachael's back from a trip to the Ladies.
I notice she's touched up her slap,
straightened her dress.
She walks up to me,
chinks our glasses,
says thanks for the wine,
then practically drags me off the bench,
saying, 'Come on, let's talk to them.
I know you want to.'
My protests are futile.
She finds us a spot
within the mingling groups.
I try to hide my blushes.
I don't think it's working.

Charlie's cornered three to herself,
including her favourite Batman,
and Claire's tossing her hair at one of the toga boys.
Sarah's with the one I thought
was trying it on before.
I hear him asking about the wedding,
so he's worked that out at least.
Even Sam is getting involved,
swaying along to the music,
and Rachael's already deep in conversation.
I stand like a lemon,
sip my drink.

I can see him standing there,
looking as awkward as me.
I give him a smile, say hello,
and we shuffle a little bit closer.
He says he saw us in the takeaway.
I tell him I saw them walk past.
He asks what I had, I say ham and cheese pizza,
well, half a pizza. He asks how it was.
It wasn't especially nice but it filled a hole.
He tells me it's not that good in there,
there's a better place down the road.
That's where they're going, after this pub,
and he can't wait. He's starving.
'Are you? I should have asked you.
Too late now.'

We mumble to silence, the subject exhausted.
I try to think of something else to say.
It takes a minute before I come up with,
'So how do you guys know each other?'
but the answer is lost as his mate approaches,
calls him a twat for no reason,
tells him they're leaving.

A sorry, a smile,
a see you later,
and he's gone.

The Library

For those still standing
another chapter begins,
but the spark is gone.
Orders grow weary, slurred,
rounds get cheaper,
as twelve turn to nine,
ten become eight.

The fallen forgotten.
No toast, no eulogy.
Instead they lament the loss
of a plastic trident,
as a solo deely bopper
bobs in mourning for its partner,
gone, who knows where.

Survivors try to revive wounded comrades.
Testosterone trials, bottles of bubbles,
an arm wrestle here, a cork popping there,
but there's medicine left undrunk,
and that might be their saviour.

Here and there a hip shakes
to music that's trying to say
this is just the beginning.
Amid cheers and jeers
and shattering glass,
boys try with girls
and girls turn away,
their phones demanding attention.
The boys move on.

Or there might be a smile,
a twist of the shoulder,
a straw sucked eye to eye,
and maybe later, just maybe,
she'll think about sharing her number,
a kiss, or more.

And for those two, a look,
across the battlefield,
him at her, her at him,
again and again and again,
but nothing more.

Then the Generals command, advance,
it's time to go, push on, move out,
and through the sudden rain
they run.

Ariel raises her hands,
scales sparkling,
lets the water take her home.

Act III

The Pack Horse

‘Callum’s round,’ says Ash.
‘Where the fuck is he?’
‘He’s gone home,’ Jonny says.
‘He passed out in the bog
at the Hyde Park.’
‘For fuck’s sake,’ says Ash. ‘Bender.
The fucking cunt owes us a fucking round.’
We make our own arrangements,
as he curses and fumes
at the falling apart of the plan
that he’d worked out so carefully.

We squeeze into the only room
that looks as if it might have space
to hold us all, those who still remain.
Callum isn’t the only one missing.
A couple of others have given up,
and two or three are struggling to continue.
It doesn’t help that we’re dripping wet,
the rain enough to soak our sheets
on a trip that can’t have been
more than thirty seconds.
‘I can see your tits,’ says Chris. He’s right.
I wish I’d used thicker material.
Water runs out of my hair, down my face.

We sit, squelching,
sighing, not talking,
Ash boiling in silent rage,
Danny trying to sneak in a nap.
Jonny looks like he needs one too.
I check if he's alright.
'Yeah,' he says, 'just tired,
and too fucking pissed.
Remind me never to do this ever again.'

There's laughter from another room,
and a band playing upstairs.
The noise of their metallic grind
jars with the sixties jukebox soul.
I can feel a headache coming on.

I look through the doorway at the girl on the bar.
She's pretty, kind of, cute but quirky,
clearly sick of the fools
she's having to deal with.
I wonder if people who work in here
dream of a job up the road,
where they'd serve a second, third drink
more often than the eleventh.

The hen party file up the corridor.
I think about going to say hello,
if only to get away from the sense
of despair that's filling our room.
Before I can move, Jonny grabs my arm,
pulls me closer, hisses in my ear,
'There's something I need to tell you.'

That's when Danny slides off his seat,
taking a table of drinks down with him.
The atmosphere shifts to noisy chaos,
and whatever Jonny was saying
is forgotten.

The Eldon

Claire insists on cocktails
and orders a pitcher of sex on the beach.
She tells us what it is three times
in case we didn't get it,
that hyena laugh as punctuation.
I ask her to pour me a small one,
but she fills the glass to the top,
and splashes some on the table while she's at it.

There's boxing on the telly
that draws in my gaze,
though I've no idea who's fighting
and couldn't care less.
Charlie's more enthusiastic,
lusting after six packs and pecs.
Sarah's looking weary.
I touch her on the shoulder,
ask if she's feeling alright.

She looks at me with wine-lit eyes,
smiles a tired smile,
says, 'Yes.'
She wraps her arms around my neck,
pulls me in, face in my ear.
I hug her back with one arm,
put my drink down safely with the other.
'Thanks for coming,' she says,
'I didn't think you would.
I'm glad you're here.'
I tell her it's fine,
and thanks for inviting me.
She tightens her grip.
I try not to show that it's hurting.

'I'm sorry about Charlie,' she says,
not as quietly as she thinks,
but the music's loud enough
to let her get away with it.
'She's awful, isn't she?
But she's my oldest friend.
We promised we'd be bridesmaids
when we were eight.'
I don't reply, just slip my other arm
into the hug.

We stay that way till a cheer erupts
from the nearest table, stealing our attention.
One of the fighters is on the floor
and the referee is counting.

The Fenton

'Fuck off, I've told you,' Ash is shouting.
'The Union's not on the Run.
It's just a copout for pussies and homos
too fucking queer to do it
fucking right.'
'You don't even like it here,' Danny says.
He's just about awake again,
saved by a tactical vomit.
'No, I fucking don't,' says Ash.
'It's a shithole fucking rockers pub
full of ugly birds
and cider-drinking cunts,
but it's on the fucking Run.'

Rant over, for now, he stops,
swigs his lager.
As if to underline his point
the jukebox plays a Maiden song.
I wonder what he'd say if he found out
I know all the words.
I stop myself from drumming my thigh,
and looking round, I realise Jonny's not here.

‘Oy oy, here we go,’ Ash starts up again.
‘Fit-tits is here and she needs a boning.’
He pushes me out of the way, heads off
to the far end of the bar, where
the hen do girls have just showed up.
The lads all relax, exhale,
exchange silent glances.

‘Where’s Jonny?’ I ask, but no one knows.
He’d seemed like he was struggling, so
I leave the group and go to find him.
I step into the corridor,
straight into the cowgirl.
‘Well fancy bumping into you,’ she says.
I laugh and say I’m sorry.
‘Having fun?’ she asks. I shrug.
‘I think I’ve had enough.’
‘Yeah,’ she says, ‘I know how you feel.’
‘It’s been a long...’ I start,
but find I’ve interrupted her
saying the exact same thing.
I stop, let her finish.
We laugh.

'We saw your mate outside,' she says.
'He's looking pretty wrecked.'
I ask if she means Jonny.
'If you say so,' she replies.
She smiles, sways,
tilts her head to the left,
and touches me just above the elbow
with two silk fingers.

I spill a bit of drink
as hands from behind me
clamp down hard on my shoulders.
I know who it is.
He pushes me down, shoves his head past my ear,
and loud enough for everyone to hear, he says,
'I wouldn't bother with this one, Grandma,
he wouldn't know what to fucking do with it.'
'Yeah, cheers Ash,' I sigh, as he roars with laughter,
removes his hands and swaggers
towards the toilets.

I wipe my wet hand on my toga.
'I should check on Jonny,' I say.
'I was looking for him, when...'
'Alright,' she says, and chinks my glass,
'I guess I'll see you later.'
'Yeah,' I say, and back away
with a wave.

Strawberryfields

'Everyone, shut up and listen!
Listen!'

Charlie's shouting as loud as she can.
If only there was a chair,
she'd surely be standing on it.
Having claimed our attention,
in a stupid put-on sing-song,
she continues.
'What we need to do now
is go around everyone
and all tell Sarah what you think of Dean.
And be honest.
Right?'

It's the worst idea I've heard all day,
but clearly it's not going to be optional.
I look around at the pictures on the wall
of John and Paul.
I love the Beatles.
If I lived round here, this might be
the kind of place I'd come to,
but at this time on a Saturday night
it feels too small, too tight,
too loud, too hot.

Claire's the first to have her say
and focuses on the physical.
'And knows what to do with it as well,'
she says, 'or that's what I've heard!'
She crumbles into laughter as Sarah protests.

I'm squashed up against a wall
with hardly room to lift my glass,
jabbed and jostled by elbows
and hips all sides.
Rachael and one of the toga boys
are making the most of the crush,
his fingers on her bum cheek,
as if it was an accident.
She presses into his chest
more than she needs to.

Charlie insists on breaking it up
when it's time to answer the question,
but Rachael swerves by claiming that
she doesn't know Dean well enough to say.
She's not alone in wanting
to avoid this conversation.
Most of the girls say something similar.
Sam elects for tact, saying,
'If Sarah thinks he's the one for her,
then that's all I need to know.'
I like her thinking, and steal the trick
when Charlie gets to me,
now visibly frustrated
that no one wants to play her stupid game.

Rachael and her new best friend
have given up on subtlety.
Smiling lips work together,
snaking arms explore their catch.
Some fat arse barges into me,
nearly knocks me flying.
He lifts a hand in false apology.
I pretend it's fine.

The question's made its way around
and now it's back to Charlie,
to have the final word in sing-song.
'I think he's great,' she says,
'and just right for Sarah,
and Claire's right, he's fit as fuck.
You know what, if Sarah wasn't
marrying him, I think I fucking would!'
She laughs. No one else does,
but Claire dives in,
'We know what you think.
We knew that when you fucked him!'

I can see I'm not the only one
who definitely didn't know that.

'What?' says Sarah, looks at Claire,
then Charlie.
I can't hear the second time,
the word she mouths obscured by music.

Charlie stares back at her,
silenced at last,
then at Claire, back at Sarah,
lips pursed as if to speak,
but nothing comes out.
Claire looks between the two,
frowning and bewildered.
'Did you not know?' she asks,
and drains her drink.

The music stops a second, two, three,
then the Beatles start to play
Helter Skelter.

The Dry Dock, part one

The last pub, thank god.
I'll be glad when we're done.
The pint that I'm poured
for the fifteenth time today
might be the least appealing I've ever had,
and yet it's welcome.
I know when I finish it,
I'm free.

We came in with the hen party,
thanks to Chris, whose tongue's spending
most of its time down one of their throats.
Jonny's in a state.
I've told him to go home,
but he says he needs to make it to the end.

His drink's not the only one untouched.
'Come on, you twats!' says Ash,
with his usual charm.
'I'm gonna be sick,' says Jonny,
and zombie-walks to the gents.

‘Where’s your bird, Ash?’ Danny asks.
‘She’s over there, waiting
for me to fuck her again.’
‘Again?’ I say, an eyebrow raised.
He thumps my arm. ‘Yes, mate,
I did her in the bogs at The Fenton.’
He thrusts his pelvis
by way of illustration.
‘Did you bollocks,’ says Danny.
‘I did,’ Ash insists,
‘and when I fuck her again later
she’s bringing her mate.’

I don’t really want to indulge his lies,
but I can’t resist a dig, so
I say, ‘That’d explain why she’s crying.’
‘Crying with fucking bliss,’ he boasts.
‘Crying because I’ve ripped her apart
with my massive fucking cock!’
He thrusts again,
this time adding a grunt.
He goes on, and I tune out.
My eyes sweep the room.

When Jonny comes out he looks as if
half his blood's been drained.
I go across to talk to him,
away from the other lads.
'You OK, mate?' I ask. 'You look like death.'
'I'm worse than that,' he says.
'I need my bed.'
'I know,' I say, 'I told you that,
but just get through this drink
and we'll get less aggro.'
'Fuck him,' he says, 'I'm off.
Where's my jacket?'
'You haven't got one,' I say,
'it's just you and your sheet.'

Jonny's drunk confusion
gives Ash a chance to attack.
He strides up, forces Jonny's pint
into his hand.
'Drink, you cunt,' he says.
'It's the last fucking pub.
You're letting the team down,
as fucking usual.'
'I can't,' says Jonny. 'I feel like shit.
I need to go home and sleep.'
'Drink, you fucking queer, come on!'
Jonny slowly shakes his head,
eyes closed, chin down.
Ash spits with rage,
'Fucking homo!'

Jonny lifts his head, opens his eyes,
leans forward, face to face with him.
'You know what?' he says.
'It's about time you knew.
I am a fucking homo,
and you are a fucking prick.'
As he speaks he shoves his pint glass
into Ash's belly, and tips it
so the whole lot soaks his toga,
dripping down his crotch and legs.
Ash steps back, looks down,
too drunk and slow to avoid the assault.

He retaliates without a word,
pushing Jonny hard in the chest,
double-handed.
Jonny's empty glass shatters on the floor,
but he's composed enough to stay on his feet.
Ash has his fist clenched,
ready to strike,
but Chris comes in first,
grabs Ash by the shoulders,
and Ash goes down,
caught off balance.

'What the fuck are you doing?' says Chris,
as security arrive.
One of the bouncers pulls Ash to his feet,
clamps his arms by his sides,
neutralised.

As he’s dragged away, he shouts,
‘Cunt’s a fucking bender!’
Jonny nods, more lively now,
grinning as he says, ‘It’s true.
I am a fucking bender!’

‘So what?’ says Chris.
Danny’s come up,
puts his hand on Jonny’s shoulder,
making sure he’s OK.
The rest of the lads gather round.

Ash has been ejected,
and none of us feel the need
to check on him.

The Dry Dock, part two

Sarah's crying,
Charlie too.
Tears, tension,
one more drink to get through.

Most of us are standing, silent,
looking at each other,
trying not to do or say
anything that might make it worse.
Sam and Claire are the only ones getting involved
and they're really not helping.

It doesn't matter how much
Charlie tries to explain
that it happened before Sarah
and Dean were together.
That's not the point,
as far as Sarah's concerned.
It's the secret that matters, she says,
how Charlie tried to hide it.

I wish they'd just drink up
and call it a night.
If they want to carry it on at the hotel,
that's up to them.
They might regret sharing a room,
but at least I can sneak off
and leave them to it.

Claire's backing Charlie up.
She didn't think it was even important,
wouldn't have mentioned it otherwise,
and she didn't know she didn't know,
and she's sorry she said anything,
but really, what's the problem?
Sam attempts the voice of reason,
but hardly a word can be heard
in this company.

Rachael's got the best idea,
wrapped up in that lad.
The perfect excuse.
The rest of us are stuck, trapped,
some of them texting people
they've no real reason to talk to.
I look at my phone. Nothing there,
and no emergency contact springs to mind.

Something's kicking off.
The toga boys.
He seems to be an innocent bystander.
It's his mate, the dickhead,
who's being taken out,
at least two pubs too late,
if they'd asked my opinion.

I finish my drink.
Done.
Thank fuck for that.
'I'm going outside,' I say.
'I'll wait for you.'

Leaving

A siren wails.
She waits.
Colder than she needs to be,
alone as she expects to be,
hat slung back, elastic slack,
she adjusts her trousers
for the thirtieth time
and watches the world.

Their world.

Stiletto heels and micro skirts,
movie stars and superheroes,
coming, going, laughing, loving,
living the end of the day like they lived the rest,
as actors,
characters.

She turns as a voice behind
says, ‘Hi,’
and she says, ‘Hey,’
something she’d never say,
usually.

‘Waiting for a cab?’ he asks,
and she says, ‘No,
just waiting for the girls.
We can walk.
You?’

'Yeah,' he says. 'It's on its way.
I've got to get Jonny home.
I'm pretty tired myself.'

She asks where he lives,
though she doesn't know the area.
He asks where they're from,
where they're staying,
though it doesn't feel important
when they still don't even know each other
by name.

And they ask if they've enjoyed their day,
and they say no, not really,
but there were moments.

Moments when it felt right,
moments when it came together,
moments when they thought
there was nowhere they'd rather be.
On that they agree.

His phone chimes.
He checks it,
says, 'That's us,'
as the getaway car pulls up.
He lifts his barely conscious friend,
says, 'It was nice to meet you,'
before bundling him in
amid contract clauses
regarding the fine to be paid
if someone is sick.

He opens the passenger door,
but instead of stepping in
he turns back.

There's one more thing
he needs to say.

Luigi says to Mario,
'We made it, bro.
We beat the game.'

Epilogue

You were here last week and the week before.
Next week we'll see you again.

The same clothes, the same drinks,
the same old scripts repeated.

That hat you bought, just for this,
we've got one here from Friday.

But we know what it'll mean to you.
We know about the magic

at the end of an Otley Run.

Other publications available from Half Moon Books

http://www.halfmoonbooks.co.uk/

Anthologies

Spokes: poetry on two wheels

The Garden: poems that grow on you

Surprise View: poems about Otley

Half Moon: poems about pubs

Poetry collections

Speak another language	Noel Whittall
Narrow Ruled Feint with Margin	Boltini
Oh, Darling Doctor Frankenstein	Pamela Scobie
The Large Ebor Collider	York Poetry Workshop
Distaff	Jane Kite

Poetry pamphlets

Play	Jo Peters
Recalculating	Gail Mosley
Life is a Long Song	Mark Connors
Travelling light	Joanna Sedgwick
Ways to wander	Peter R White
The flank of a fish	Rosalind York
earth and universe	Marjorie Burgoyne Sedgwick
New Lease	Sandra Burnett
Written on the skin	Bill Fitzsimons
Israel-Palestine	Bruce Barnes
know-it-all	Dan Whittaker
If Moments Were Places	Alicia Fernández
Killing the Piano	Joe Williams
The sky is cracked	Sarah L Dixon
the necessary line	Nick Allen
Proper Poems	John Coopey
Letters to a first love from the future	Andy Armitage
After the raging	Barbara Howerska
Sounding for home	Rachel Kerr

Poetry Plays

Town below the steps	Matthew Hedley Stoppard *et al*